GALF GAMES

By Roger Hurn

Illustrated by
Anthony Williams

Titles in the Zipwire series:

Who Are You?	David Orme
3Dee	Danny Pearson
Doom Clone	Melanie Joyce
Too Risky!	Alison Hawes
Wanda Darkstar	Jane A C West
Galactic Games	Roger Hurn
Robot Eyes	Jillian Powell
Charlie's Tin	Lynda Gore
Run For Your Life	Jonny Zucker
Changing Rooms	Melanie Joyce

Badger Publishing Limited
Oldmedow Road, Hardwick Industrial Estate,
King's Lynn PE30 4JJ
Telephone: 01553 769209
www.badgerlearning.co.uk

2 4 6 8 10 9 7 5 3 1

Galactic Games ISBN 978-1-78837-605-1

Text © Roger Hurn 2011
Complete work © Badger Publishing Limited 2021

Badger Publishing would like to thank Jonny Zucker for his help in putting this series together.

Commissioning Editor: Sarah Rudd
Editor: Claire Morgan
Typesetting: Adam Wilmott
Illustration: Anthony Williams
Page 32 illustration: Juliet Breese
Cover design: Shaun Page
Font: OpenDyslexic

GALACTIC GAMES

Contents

Badger LEARNING

Chapter 1

Jack Swift is the star of the hit
TV series *Sci-Fi Spy Guy*.

Jack has a big secret.

His starship from the TV show is real!

It's called STEALTH.

Jack wants to take STEALTH for a ride around the galaxy.

He has two hours before everyone arrives to start filming the new *Sci-Fi Spy Guy* adventure.

"OK, STEALTH. Take me somewhere interesting," says Jack.

This is Jack's first mistake!

Chapter 2

STEALTH blasts off.

Jack feels like he is being turned inside out.

Jack's head stops spinning at last.

STEALTH is next to a big planet.

Suddenly, a ray of bright purple light shoots up from the planet's surface.

Jack dives under his seat and waits for the explosion.

Nothing happens.

Jack relaxes.

Jack thinks the ray is harmless.

This is Jack's second mistake!

It is an alien tractor beam.

It has STEALTH trapped!

Chapter 3

The tractor beam pulls STEALTH down to the surface of the planet.

STEALTH lands with a bump.

The starship's door slides open and Jack steps outside.

A female alien greets him.

"Hello Jack. Welcome to Planet Loki. My name is Akra."

Akra says everyone in the galaxy loves watching *Sci-Fi Spy Guy* on TV.

Jack thinks Akra is just a fan.

This is **Jack's** third mistake!

Akra is in charge of the Galactic
Games.

Akra tells Jack that he must
take part in a BMX bike race
against her champion.

Jack likes riding BMX bikes.

"OK," he says, "I'll do it."

This is Jack's fourth mistake!

"This is no ordinary BMX race. It's the Life or Death Anti-Grav BMX Race," says Akra.

Jack's blood runs cold.

"Life or death?" he repeats.

Akra smiles.

"If you win, your prize will be to go home. If you lose, you will be zapped to death!" she says.

Chapter 4

Jack tells Akra he has changed his mind.

He does not want to race.

Akra shrugs.

"You still have to do it!"
she says.

Jack walks back to STEALTH.

He is worried.

Jack has not ridden an anti-grav
BMX before.

They can fly!

Then Jack has an idea.

He needs to write an *anti* anti-
grav program.

Then he can go down as well as up!

Jack loads the new program onto his phone.

An alien voice on STEALTH's speaker tells Jack he must come to the anti-grav BMX track.

The race is about to start.

Chapter 5

Jack lines up at the start of
the race with the anti-grav
BMX champion.

The champion sneers at Jack.

"You're going to be zapped,"
she says.

Jack gulps.

Things are not looking good.

The race starts.

The champion zooms up into
the sky.

Jack does his best to follow.

Suddenly, the champion flies
straight at Jack.

She flips Jack's front wheel.

She is cheating!

Jack's bike spins out of control.

He is hanging upside down.

He is going to crash!

The champion laughs.

Jack is angry.

He grits his teeth and flips back onto his seat.

He loops the loop.

The crowd gasps.

The champion is far ahead.

It is now or never.

Time to use the new program!

Jack pulls out his phone and
aims it at the champion's bike.

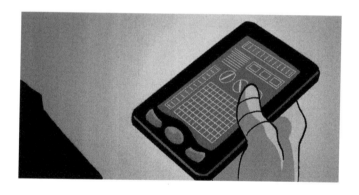

Her bike stops in mid-air.

It crashes to the ground.

Jack wins the race and the crowd goes wild.

Akra has to let Jack go.

Jack flies STEALTH home, ready for the next adventure.

Questions

What is the name of Jack's starship? *(page 6)*

What is Jack's first mistake? *(page 8)*

What will happen to Jack if he loses the race? *(page 16)*

Who wins the race? *(page 28)*

Zipwire

Looking for your next read?

Have a look at all the great books in the Zipwire series

badgerlearning.co.uk @badgerlearning